Leaf Books
Young Writers'
Anthology

XVIII

First published by Leaf Books Ltd in 2009

www.leafbooks.co.uk

Leaf Books Ltd.
GTi Suite,
Valleys Innovation Centre,
Navigation Park,
Abercynon,
CF45 4SN

Printed by Jem
www.jem.co.uk

ISBN-10: 1-905599-51-X
ISBN-13: 978-1-905599-51-6

About Leaf Books

Leaf Books' fine and upstanding mission is to support the publication of high quality short fiction, micro-fiction and poetry by both new and established writers.

We have put over 300 authors and poets into print since our inception in 2006. Many of them have never been published before.

See our website at www.leafbooks.co.uk for news, more information about our authors, other titles and having your own work published by Leaf.

Other Leaf Books Anthologies

The Better Craftsman and Other Stories
The Final Theory and Other Stories
Razzamatazz and Other Poems
Outbox and Other Poems
The Light That Remains and Other Short Stories
Dogstar and Other Science Fiction Stories
Derek and More Micro-Fiction
Coffee and Chocolate
Naked Thighs and Cotton Frocks and Other Stories
The Someday Supplement
Imagine Coal and More Micro-Fiction
Standing on the Cast-Iron Shore and Other Poems
Discovering a Comet and More Micro-Fiction
Dancing with Delsie and Other Poems
Ada and More Nano-Fiction

Contents

Introduction   8

Under 11 age category
Winner

The Great Barrier Reef   Hugo Grundy   10

Runner-up

Sicilian Adventure   Dualtagh Grundy   12

Colours are for ….   Gemma Baker   13

The Amazing Pebble   Archie Clark   14

Mr Leroy's Grand Days Out   Carley Ann Hayes   15

Mysteries and Mirrors   Ellamae Hindley   16

My Wales   Ruby Johnston   17

Snow   Shayahi   18
                                  Kathirgamanathan

Pet Dinos in my Garden   Jonathan Potter   19

I've Never Seen   John Roberts   20

The Ghost Galleon   Imogen Shortall   21

 Avril   Hector Stellyes   22

Doors   Hector Stellyes   23

The Sand Witch   Mollie Thomas   24

Rebellious Megan   Sumeyya Tontus   25

What does my Daddy do at work?   Dominic Wills   26

After Dark   Evan James Ward   27

Mind your Manners   Evan James Ward   27

Under 14 age category
Winner

The Taste of a Tic Tac	Henry Gould	30

Runner-up

How can I look forward when I don't know where to go?	Shakira Dyer	31
Katia's Story	Bethany Barnes	32
Sights of Newport	Saskia Barnett	33
Darkness	Selena Drake	34
Garden Exploration	Shakira Dyer	35
Geraint and the Lady of the Lake	Konrad Edwards	37
New Life	Henry Gould	38
The Trenches	Ellie Hendricks	39
Weekends	Oscar Lowe	40
They Don't See What I See	Cleo Mathias	41
Surfing	Sam Moore	42
The River	Creative Writing Club, Penryn College	43
Leprechaun Holiday	Cerren Richards	44

18 and Under age category
Winner

Journey in the Countryside	Phoebe Power	46

Runner-up

Writer's Block	Mairi Templeton	47
All I Need Is Inspiration …	Louise Hunter	49
Reality	Louise Hunter	50
Deliveries	Amy Pay	51
An Education	Charles Risius	52
Regifting	Mairi Templeton	53
History, Period Two	Luke Webber	54

Introduction

Leaf Books Young Writers' Anthology contains all the winning poems and short stories from the Leaf Books' Young Writers competition of 2009. The competition was judged according to three age categories: 'under 11', 'under 14' and '18 and under'. We received an impressive number of entries in every age range and from all over the country, and we whittled it down to this excellent collection of winning and commended entries.

Our congratulations to all the young writers who made it into this anthology: each of you wrote something that made us laugh or made us think or made us jealous of your talent, and in one or two cases made us say 'Are you really only seven?' in incredulous voices (and you really were). There's a wonderful range of topics and styles to be discovered within: from eight-year-old Archie Clark's dreamlike story 'The Amazing Pebble' to fifteen-year-old Louise Hunter's lyrical poem 'Reality', and many more besides. We very much hope you enjoy reading through them.

Our most special congratulations must go to the three winners and the three runners-up. Hugo Grundy won the 'under 11' category with his astonishingly accomplished free verse poem 'The Great Barrier Reef'; his equally talented brother Dualtagh Grundy was the runner-up with his poem 'Sicilian Adventure'. The two poems were real standouts and we were frankly astonished to see such mature, individual voices in two such young boys. Remember their names. The winner in the '14 and under' category was Henry Gould with his touching poem 'Taste of a Tic-Tac' about the death of a beloved grandfather; the runner-up was Shakira Dyer with her poem 'How Can I Look Forward When I Don't Know Where to Go?', an impressively thematic verse for one so young and with a real idea behind it. And last but not least, the winner and runner-up in the '18 and under' category: Phoebe Power, for her evocative imagistic poem 'Journey in the Countryside' and Mairi Templeton for her comical, reflexive and highly empathetic story 'Writer's Block'. All six were real standouts and we hope the authors and poets – all of them – continue to write, to develop and to have a lot of fun in the process.

The competition was judged by the Leaf Books team. Our thanks to all who entered.

Under 11
age category

The Great Barrier Reef
(My baby brother)
by Hugo Grundy, aged 7 (Winner)

I am a thin plastic tube.
I feed him through his nose.
Water – buds of it – squeezes of it
landing on his lips.

He is very bald.
Thin arms, short legs, sticky things all over him
like a fungus.

Light above him – blanket beneath him – machine behind him
liney and beepy like a ship or an aeroplane.

He's dreaming about being a man
about having brothers – flying and aeroplanes.

And all he knows is that I am there.

Mum – hands up to her face
putting air in – huh, huh, huh for house!.

(Oisín walks in. He's in his orange puffy jacket.
He's laughing! He thinks that's him in there!)

He stops moving – he stops moving
for two days and two nights – that's … 32 hours.

He's dreaming he's the Great Barrier Reef.
Gigantic and still.

He wakes in the night and he's laughing
and nobody is there
except hundreds of himself.

Are there hundreds of him all clapping
and bursting out laughing?

Sicilian Adventure
by Dualtagh Grundy, aged 8 (Runner-up)

One hot summer.

The ground was dusty
like a rocky chimney.
Thousands of ants
carrying heavy rubble.

We were five brothers in Sicily.

The air – a volcano emptying
its hot breath.
Our bodies – boiled and parched.
Freezing, spraying footbaths
like the Atlantic ocean
feeling scared.

Chiara was a girl like a lioness.
She was our friend.
Said I had blue eyes
like the moon.

A lady, Lara from Palermo
gave us a water pistol
and sugar-coated nuts carried away by ants,
took my two brothers
to the shower
and washed them.

On the air
pink ribbony silk waving.
Accompanying insect buzzing
trees.

Colours are for ....
by Gemma Baker, aged 8

Brown is for the brown wrinkly logs,
Red is for the red soft roses,
Yellow is for the yellow bumpy cone of an ice-cream,
Blue is for the blue wavy seal's home,
Orange is for my guinea pig's orange velvety coat,
White is for the flapping white coat of a duck,
Grey is for the cracked grey walls of the church,
Black is for my short black skirt from school,
Purple is for the cosy purple walls of my bedroom,
Green is for the fresh green grass in the fields,
Turquoise is for the summery turquoise seas,
Violet is for the tiny violet flowers in the garden,
Dark green is for the floppy dark green seaweed,
Dark brown is for the dark brown bird-like rooftops,
Pink is for the pink scruffy face of a pig,
EVERY COLOUR IS IN MY RAINBOW!

The Amazing Pebble
by Archie Clark, aged 8

One day, I was walking in the park and I saw a strange looking pebble. It was blue, yellow, orange, brown, purple and green all in one pebble. I picked it up. It was warm and my hands were cold. I rubbed it. Suddenly I was going around in circles. I landed with a bump. I saw trees made of chocolate, buildings made of doughnuts, cars made of strawberries and as I walked along I saw people made of chewing gum.

The people were chewing themselves! I couldn't believe it. It was so funny. I looked up and there was a Smartie airplane. It dropped loads of Smarties on me. Clatter, clatter, clatter! I was trapped under all the Smarties. I rubbed my pebble, but it didn't work. I shouted, 'If I don't get out of here in a minute I'll break my spine.'

I was scared. There was only one way to get out. Eat my way out! I eventually got out. I felt very sick and I was covered in all the colours of the Smarties. I looked just like my pebble. I was missing my brother and my parents. Suddenly the express bus came around the corner and I said 'Bus!' The bus stopped and I got on it. It was made of cherries and meringues. It took me home.

Mr Leroy's Grand Days Out
by Carley Ann Hayes, aged 11 (10 at the time of writing)

As some of you may know, Mr Leroy is the world's first and only blob of living bubblegum! Dun – Dun – Duun!
He has led a very interesting life and has lots of wonderful tales to tell, such as:

Getting stuck on someone's shoe and travelling all the way to Chicago in America before managing to escape by blowing himself up!

Or how about the time when he got stuck on the wing of an aeroplane and befriended two seagulls named Terrence and Bob, who mercifully rescued him but accidentally dropped him onto the very top of the Empire State Building! Terrified about how he could possibly get down, Mr Leroy remembered he had his mobile 'phone – Hallelujah!

Immediately he rang his best friend Percy the tortoise, who straight away, as fast as he could (not very!), got on the first 'plane to New York and courageously went and rescued poor Mr Leroy – who had been up there for three whole days – by calling a fire engine and climbing up an enormous ladder. But the ladder was still not big enough, so Percy decided there was one way to save Mr Leroy.

He scaled the building to the top with a long rope and then as soon as Percy got to the top, he tied the rope around himself and Mr Leroy and the other end of the rope to the Empire State Building. They both bungee jumped off the building and then the firemen cut them loose. Mr Leroy had almost starved to death, so he had to stay in hospital for a week and then they were both allowed to fly back home to England INSIDE THE PLANE!

Mysteries and Mirrors
by Ellamae Hindley

The mirrors with their hope, their mysteries they hide
Touching, touching
The ghostly mists of the moonbow
A ribbon of moonlight dances
As he carries me on the wings of the night across the jewelled
skies and then the darkness comes
Haunting, haunted

The darkness haunting with faded images.
Our hearts thump against our chests
His voice becomes just a whisper
His face so white and peaked
Fading, fading

Reaching out he kissed her
The bomb had fallen
Covered with their own red blood
They cry … A silence fills the air
God called them as they closed their eyes
They heard their final calling
Their hands so closed and interwined
Sleeping, sleeping

Little did they seek what would happen on this night
The street, their love burned so tragically tonight
The mirrors with their hope, their mysteries they hide
Uncovering the stories of war from which they could not survive.

My Wales
by Ruby Johnston, aged 11 (10 at the time of writing)

I've seen a lake with a mountain's reflection glistening on its
   face.

I've heard the dizzy singing of bees as they frantically work,
darting in and out of the shining, yellow daffodils.

I've climbed in pain to the highest peak.
Just to see the red dragon fly and blow hot red, orange and
   yellow breath into the sky.

I've smelt the wonderful Welsh cakes trickling and tempting
my taste buds as they bubble and brown in grandma's kitchen.

I've felt the feeling of pride of being a Welsh citizen.

Snow
by Shayahi Kathirgamanathan, aged 9

It falls upon the wooden poles
and is shaped like a tureen.
It glides upon the once
green trees and freezes their leaves.

The snowflakes are swift
though, they drift gently.
The snow has padded
the roofs with cushioned sheets.

The door handles are cold
and dripping with frost.
The green grass is lost
and plants are large lumps.

The children play in delight
however grey the sky may be.
The adults sit in armchairs
with a mug of tea.

Pet Dinos in my Garden
by Jonathan Potter, aged 10

Argentinosaurus
Is very big and tall.
I have one in my garden
And I have called him Paul.

Tyrannosaurus aren't
The biggest predators.
I have one in my garden
And I have called him George.

Giganotosaurus
Liked to eat fresh meat.
I have one in my garden
And I have called him Pete.

I have three pets in my garden
But not Dinosaurs at all.
They're actually baby rabbits
That are very cute and small.

But rabbits are so boring.
They don't have snarling jaws.
They're too soft and fluffy.
I want dinosaurs!

I've Never Seen
by John Roberts, aged 10

I've never seen the martians invade earth.
I've never seen a monster give birth.

I've never seen a mouse chase a cat.
I've never seen a monkey use a bat.

I've never seen a rhino learn karate.
I've never seen a snail throw a party.

I've never seen a bee not make honey.
I've never seen a slug use money.

I've never seen a snake that isn't scary.
I've never seen a fish that is hairy.

I've never seen a gorilla in love with a bean.
I've never seen what I've never seen.

The Ghost Galleon
by Imogen Shortall, aged 10

I was walking across the soft ground of Holcombe Sands when I noticed something. The moon. Except it wasn't a moon anymore. It was a galleon. Three majestic wooden masts, three beautiful silk sails and a shape to be proud of. It was a most odd sight.

The boat had almost landed. It was a ghostly white and sent thousands of moonbeams lighting up the night sky.

Something told me to hide. The ship didn't look very inviting so I fumbled around in the dark and found a small crack in the cliff, just big enough for my size. Without thinking I squeezed in.

Just a few seconds after I had found my hiding place a hoard of armed seamen disembarked from the boat. The first thing I noticed was that they were shimmering like the moon.

Ghosts.

Without thinking I grabbed a sharp piece of flint and hurled myself onto the ground before them. Immediately the leader drew a shining gold sword.

'En garde,' I growled as I raised my weapon high and began to fight.

The ghost was good. He thrust, parried, and then jabbed. It was all I could to stop myself being hit. But suddenly I did something I never dreamed I could do. I slipped on the wet floor but in doing so my feet collided with the ghost's legs. Suddenly the ghost's legs disappeared. Of course! They vanished when you touched them! I grabbed the gold sword and began to hack into the rock of the cliff. The soft limestone easily gave way and smashed the army of ghosts. They all perished.

Sitting on the floor, I ran my finger over the shining gold blade and wondered what price a ghost's sword would fetch.

Avril

By Hector Stellyes, aged 8

You are the red dashing in a painting
You are the spag-bol on my plate
You are the hot chocolate freshly poured
You are my room just how I like it

You are the breakfast dribbling down my chin
You are the bluebell swaying in the breeze
You are the good tree to climb in summer
You are the plum just picked, giving out your juice

You are the sun on a summer's day
You are the science lesson going on forever
You are the orange peeling off your skin
You are the blackness in the night

You are my favourite book half way through
You are the sun in Turkey
You are my favourite game, which is everlasting

Doors
By Hector Stellyes, aged 8

Doors in my house,
Doors in my garden
Mum said
'There shouldn't be doors in the garden'
So I piled them all up on the
Fridge and said
'Happy now?'

The Sand Witch

by Mollie Thomas, aged 11 (10 at time of writing)

Sandie lived underneath the sand on Pobbles beach. She had built a small cottage there where she slept, played and caught her food! Her favourite food was little Welsh boys who tasted even better if they were wearing their Welsh costumes. She loved the crunch as she bit down on sandy toes as well as the taste of little girls' pigtails. Of course, sometimes they tasted horrible like one rounded spoilt child who Sandie just happened to take a bite out of.

One day in December when no one was on the beach, she noticed a crab. Seeing that there was nothing better to eat she grabbed it and started to munch. Just then a small boy covered in freckles walked down the beach to where Sandie's underground cottage lay. Freckly boys are heaven to Sand Witches; they are just like eating a chocolate digestive. Sandie's nose flicked up and started to fly all over the place like a hound dog on pursuits. Her hand reached up from the sand and slowly grabbed the boy's foot. She could taste it already, as the boy's head just appeared through the thick sand. His best friend emerged confused and weary beside him panting and wagging his tail.

'Hello little boy,' cackled Sandie happily.

'Don't eat me,' cried the boy, whose name was Efan. 'My friend is much tastier'. Sandie eyed his friend up and down. He wasn't pretty but he would do. She grabbed his tail and began to eat. Efan saw the opportunity to leave and did without a backward glance. He had trouble explaining to his parents why he hadn't brought back his dog. Would they believe that a Sand Witch had eaten him?

One thing is for certain; Efan never went to Pobbles beach again!

Rebellious Megan
by Sumeyya Tontus, aged 10

'Answer something!' whispered Lily, as she nudged me repeatedly. 'Do you want to go outside or not?' I groaned. Our teacher was doing that thing when you can only go out to play once you have answered a question. I hate getting detention or staying inside, but I hate answering questions equally. Lily has answered a question, now. Eight times seven. Of course, I am not dumb so I know the answer, it's just I hate putting my hand up and answering. It makes me feel horrible.

'What is two times two?' asked Miss Davies, looking at me especially. A few people sniggered. They all think I'm stupid. Just because I don't respond to any questions, doesn't mean I am dumb. 'Megan?' said Miss Davies, staring at me.

'Three, miss,' I replied, grinning. Of course, I answered wrong on purpose, and Miss Davies knew that too. She then started to get furious.

'Megan Stewart!' she shouted across the classroom, 'get to detention, immediately!' I didn't start sobbing, like Sarah Howards would do. I just shrugged my shoulders and walked out the room. I didn't walk right, towards the grey, dirty detention room doors, but I walked left, towards the main entrance. Luckily for me, there was no teacher behind the messy desk. As I walked closer to the automatic doors, they opened. I walked off, like I didn't care. I didn't care, actually. Not one bit. As I walked out of the school, I saw Lily on the playground. Fortunately, no one saw me, except Lily. She mouthed, 'Megan?' I know she was wondering if she should tell me off, but even Lily wouldn't do that. She was too trustworthy, even if she is a goody two shoes. She was astonished by my behaviour. Everyone else would be too.

What does my Daddy do at work?
by Dominic Wills, aged 9

My Daddy says he is a doctor.
But I don't believe him.
I think he's a super-spy,
Disguising himself as a normal passer-by
And sorting out any crime.

Or, he could drive a jet plane, swooping over the land, engine
    roaring.
But maybe he tests computer games, is a jungle explorer or
    even a star England footballer?

It is beyond me what Daddy is.
All I can be sure of is that he doesn't have a normal job.

After Dark
by Evan James Ward, aged 6

Outside after dark
rough badgers bury and foxes howl.
After Dark, after dark.

In here after dark
bats swoop and
scary skeletons rustle.
After dark after dark.

Under the covers after dark
I cuddle my teddy and
I am sleeping peacefully.
After dark after dark.

Mind your Manners
by Evan James Ward, aged 6

Don't throw your food.
Don't smash the mirrors.
Don't get in a mood.
Don't tease the gorillas.

Say please and thank you.
Say sorry if you're cross.
Remember to share your toys.
You're not the boss.

Under 14 age category

The Taste of a Tic Tac
by Henry Gould, aged 12 (Winner)

I remember
His wise age-old eyes
Shrivelled apple-skin smiles
Inquisitive nose and thinning snowy hair
And placid voice with steady laughter.

I remember
His minty tic tac breath
The shiny beads of berries we collected
His eager eyes reflected the sun
Our special fruity jam.

I remember
The thoughtful gifts he gave me
Long absorbing stories
Shimmering coins for my collection
And visits to his old university Cambridge.

I also remember
The yoghurty smell of his sick bed
Gnarled twig-like limbs
Tired frail watery eyes
And pale rippled skin.

After these fond memories
His house seemed empty
My tic tac tasted sour
I thought about his happy life
And salty tears enclosed the world.

How can I look forward when I don't know where to go?
by Shakira Dyer, aged 11

How can I look forward when I don't know where to go?
It should be easier to go back because I do know where I've been.
If I could go back I could re-read books
without giving my favourites back to the library.
I could re-watch films
without thought of the rental date.
I could re-eat chocolate
without realising I had finished it.
Oh the things I could do if I could go back.
I could perhaps make a replica of my old friend
without her having to move away.

If I could go back, I would rub that bit out.
But, if I never went forward
I couldn't learn new words in new books,
see new films,
or learn the taste of new chocolate.
It would always be the same old
And I would never make new friends.
So … I have come to a conclusion,
And it isn't that hard.
Going forward is easier said than done.
But after I go forward and try it out
I really do know where to go.

Katia's Story
by Bethany Barnes, aged 12

Train stations.

What do you think of when you hear this?

Does it make you think of *wizzy wooshy* fast trains, children laughing and everyone's tickets being sucked in by MASSIVE ticket machines?

Or maybe it reminds you of dirty floors, sticky seats, smelly toilets and the odd piece of fresh chewing gum under a damp wooden bench?

But I don't care, I can't care, I have no choice…I live here. Me, my brother, sister and dad live in Waterloo train station.

My dad says 'Well, at least we live under a roof…' but I know better. I'm thirteen, old enough to know that we *are* broke.

Sometimes I see those pretty girls, my age, tossing their long hair at me, with their hoop earrings and silver bank bags. I am not like them … I never will be. I try not to cry because if I do it will draw attention to me so I hide my frail face under my sleeping bag.

I bet right now you will be feeling sorry for me, but you will be pleased to know things have changed… since a help the homeless charity saw us, took us in, got my dad a job and us a school.

They didn't forget about a house though!

We're living in a small cottage called Bran-bury cottage. I've got my own room…something I've wanted ever since I was born!

The house isn't much. But it's ours. Our home.
My home.

Sights of Newport
by Saskia Barnett, aged 12

A puddle of rainwater
Like God has lost a close friend
Why else would the heavens rain?
Graffiti on the walls
A great artist's crime
Art or disaster?
Pick.

Darkness
by Selena Drake, aged 13

I have dreamt this dream before. I see the people of my tribe, labouring over daily chores. Nothing seems wrong, until everything changes. Suddenly, all I see is darkness. It smothers the camp, and for a moment I see nothing. Then I hear screams. I see the innocent and terrified faces of all in my tribe, and I am unable to help them. I can do nothing but watch them suffer.

I have a gift. Every time I dream these strange dreams, it always happens. I was able to save my tribe from being ambushed by enemies, and when I advised them to store more food, they did not suffer from hunger. I went to the chief earlier, and for the first time he refused to move camp. He was too scared to believe me. I saw the fear in his eyes.

I now pack my belongings into a small leather bag. I must escape, and bring as many people as possible. I have convinced my friend, Robin, to come with me. My family will come as well. No one else will come. We will leave tonight, without anyone knowing.

An hour ago we left camp. We all know that we will not see it again. We do not know what will happen, but they will all die. No lives will be spared. We sit on a high mountain, far enough to keep us safe, yet close enough for us to view camp. Our breaths are held, and our hearts thump quickly. Everything is quiet, and the sky is black. Suddenly, I see something black, stretching towards the camp. I cry out, but I cannot drown out the screams of my people. I do not know what that darkness was, but it has destroyed the lives of my people.

Garden Exploration
by Shakira Dyer, aged 11

'… Do you see anything, Explorer Bert?'

'Nothing, Explorer Ellie,' replied Bert through his walkie-talkie. 'Wait, here comes your sister!'

'Ellie!' called Tess.

'What?' Ellie asked.

The explorer game stopped. The circling vultures became normal, every-day pigeons. The vines turned back to bushes and flowers. The ferocious tiger was Tess.

'Can I play?' Tess shouted.

'Well, ok,' Ellie muttered. She looked through the toilet roll. 'Oh, no!' she cried. 'Tess is getting attacked by a rhinoceros!'

'That's no rhinoceros!' Tess giggled. 'It's Rosie!'

The 'rhinoceros' barked and licked Tess' cheek.

Ellie pulled Tess free.

'What's our mission, Explorer Ellie?' called Bert.

'Hm, we have to swim across the lake, walk through a slimy swamp, then climb up the mountain and we'll meet at the other side of the jungle.'

'Let's go!' Ellie cried to Tess.

Soon they got to the lake.

'Watch out for alligators,' screamed Bert.

'I don't see any alligators,' Tess interrupted, looking at the paddling pool.

'These alligators are hiding underwater,' said Ellie.

'Oh,' Tess said.

'Now we must be careful across the …' started Ellie, but then Rosie barked and splashed into the mud.

'No, Rosie!' Ellie cried.

'Woof!' woofed Rosie.

'There's a swamp monster living down there,' Ellie told her

little sister. 'If we wake him, he could eat us up.'

Tess stayed close to Ellie.

'What's that noise?' whispered Tess

'Run!'

They ran quickly across the garden until they reached the treehouse.

'Hold onto this rope and I'll pull you up the mountain!' shouted Bert.

'I like crossing the jungle,' Tess said.

'Yap!' barked Rosie from the bottom of the treehouse.

'Did you have fun?' Mum asked. Then she took one look at Rosie and said, 'Rosie, I think it's time for a bath.'

Geraint and the Lady of the Lake
By Konrad Edwards, aged 13

Geraint sat on the edge of the misty, grey lake. He wondered how it had happened; it had been so fast. Men with swords had come, running into his hamlet, shouting strange words. 'Sea raiders!' a village man had shouted, before they cut him down. Geraint had been playing when the men arrived and suddenly houses had been burning, people screaming, crying, dying. His mother had come to him and told him to run and not to stop until he was far away, then she had kissed him and said good-bye, with a deep, sad look on her face. Geraint couldn't understand why. He had run, and run, and eventually decided that he was tired, and had come a long way, so he stopped: now he was here.

Then, something Geraint had never seen before happened; the mist thinned and a silhouette appeared. The strange thing about the silhouette was it was coming across the lake! Geraint felt a little afraid, but he knew that his mother would come for him soon, so he sat and waited.

Eventually, the silhouette moved into view. It was a tall, odd-looking woman; she came and sat next to Geraint, and though he didn't know her, he felt safer. When she spoke it was in a gentle, calming voice: 'You are safe now, child,' she said, 'come with me.'

'No,' replied Geraint firmly, 'Mummy will come and get me soon.'

'She cannot, child,' said the woman, 'she has gone where neither of us will gladly follow. I will care for you and raise you in her stead. Now come.' She spoke with the same gentleness as before, but with a hint of command.

The little boy followed meekly, holding her hand as he went.

New Life
by Henry Gould, aged 12

Crystal silence embraced the house and the stars held their breath. The trees froze and the night was still. Suddenly a shrill yell penetrated the tranquillity.

I heard muffled voices coming from my parents' room. Mum was moaning and Dad was mumbling on the phone. Disorientated I lumbered across the hallway to my dad. I asked what was going on and he told me not to worry, but the glistening beads of sweat told me that it wasn't all right.

The crunch of gravel on the driveway interrupted my confusion. The door-bell rang and a man in a white coat burst in with a little mask around his mouth, shouting, 'Where is she?'

He rushed upstairs into the bedroom and frantic whispers echoed around, accompanied by wails and screams. I put my ear to the door to see what was going on, but all I could hear were grunts and groans. Shadows danced underneath the doorway and after many moans something told me that Mum was in terrible pain.

Dad came out and I barged past him into the room. I looked across the bed and saw Mum struggling to hold a small writhing object, with a defeated look on her face. It had a small purple face with screwed-up eyes. Pink hands were flailing and then, it let out an ear-piercing howl.

'What is that thing?!' I shouted.

'That thing is your little brother, Henry,' Dad replied. My stomach knotted and my wail entwined with the baby's, out into the pale grey of the morning sky.

The Trenches
by Ellie Hendricks, aged 12

He sits in the trenches
With the corpses he lies
Quiet in wait
As rats scuttle by

His head aches in terror
His fingers are numb
Fifteen years of age
Yet armed with a gun

His legs are exhausted
With every effort he stands
The bodies surround him
And blood on his hands

He looks round in sorrow
At the friends he has lost
The heroic soldiers
That are now left to rot

He knew it was coming
So in dead of night
He ran out to greet
Now one less in the fight

We fight for our people
We fight and we lie
We live for our country
And for our country we die

Weekends
by Oscar Lowe, aged 13

We like to get out and about
at weekends, me and my dad.
Doing lots of super things,
– some of the best times I've ever had.

Pottering about in ponds and fountains,
walking in the dales, moors and mountains,
playing football, going to the park,
calling on friends and having a lark.
Climbing trees, exploring caves,
running along the beach and jumping in the waves.
Flying kites and playing cricket,
travelling on trains with a weekend ticket.

'All these weekends,'
sneers our neighbour Mr Lonsbar,
'when one should have been
cleaning and polishing one's car.'

Mr Lonsbar spends his weekends cleaning;
with him it's such a fad.
His car is bright and fresh and gleaming –
but he's not as happy as me and my dad.

They Don't See What I See
by Cleo Mathias, aged 11

I begged and begged my parents all week to let me add the Tate Modern to our possible trips list, so when it was my turn to choose where we went on family day (every second Saturday of the month) it would be allowed. They caved on Thursday evening. This really annoyed my brother Josh because Liverpool were playing Manchester United and he would have to miss it.

'Why can't I have Imogen's go?' he whined. 'The Tate Modern is soooo boring!'

'Because that wouldn't be fair,' replied Mum. 'You've had your go. Remember Dinosaur World, hmm?'

'I don't think we'll be forgetting that in a hurry!' chuckled Dad, trying to keep his eyes on the road.

An hour later we were inside the Tate, wandering around in awe at all the masterpieces. Well, at least I was.

'Look at this silly thing,' snorted Dad in disgust,

'Just a pile of metal and rubbish!' said Mum, holding her nose in the air. Josh just grinned. They were looking at a metal fish covered in crisp packets.

'I think the artist was trying to say that pollution in the sea is killing off the sea creatures,' I suggested.

'Nonsense,' said Mum and Dad in unison.

'Yeah, stupid,' said Josh.

'Just a hunk of junk!' murmured Dad.

My heart sank. I see the world through pictures, not through words. They don't see what I see.

Surfing
by Sam Moore, aged 12

The sea is as calm as a millpond.
The golden sun is reflecting off the water.
I sit there waiting,
Waiting, like a lion about to pounce.
The breeze is gentle like a dolphin.

Suddenly, the millpond turns to an ocean.
The lion pounces and the dolphin turns to a shark,
As the waves get bigger.
I jump on my azure blue, eight-foot surfboard,
And start to paddle.

I stand up on my surfboard
And ride the towering, turquoise wave.
The cold spray flies into my face
And the journey begins.

The beach gets closer,
As the wave begins to break.
The wave crashes,
And turns to paper-white foam.

The soft, beige sand,
Only a stone's-throw away.
I finally reach the shore and get off my board.
The waves are smashing against the shoreline.
Another ride on nature's rollercoaster and I am ready to go again.

The River

by Izella Holliday, Molly Johnstone-Clark, Georgie Phillips, Cora Griffin, Zoe Brooks and Mark Ryan, aged 11 and 12 (students of the Creative Writing Club, Penryn College)

The river like a glassy pathway cutting through coniferous forests,
leading the way for salmon rushing to get home,
it cuts maliciously through the earth, slicing countries in half,
yet she brings pleasure to those who gaze upon her glassy face.

The river like a mirror of the sky,
Bright and Blue,
Reflecting her beauty,
From one majestic surface to another.
The river a long ribbon of a dancer's shoe,
As dainty as her pointed toe,
Curling round her endless journey
Like her dance.
The rivers are like veins from the earth,
Plastered to her face in an abstract manner,
entwined beneath the skin,
Blood flowing through, a source to stay alive.
The river is a prisoner,
A prisoner of the forest,
Stuck between both sides,
Surrounded by arched trees.
The river, like the sorrowful tears of the mountain,
Streaming down her stricken face,
Leaving her skin cracked and cavernous,
Hidden beneath a veil of luscious green silk.

Leprechaun Holiday
by Cerren Richards, aged 13

Garry was a normal boy – well, if you can call Garry normal. He had bright red hair and he dressed like a leprechaun.

Every year Garry would go on a family holiday to Ireland with Boris and Doris, his parents, because Garry believed that leprechauns lived there. When they got there Garry would be looking for them non stop like a bird trying to find food, but unlike the bird Garry would never find a leprechaun. But this year they were going to Spain because his parents had had enough of Ireland and the bad weather, whether Garry liked it or not.

When Garry's parents told him that they were going to Spain instead of Ireland he felt his heart fall and his smile turn into a frown. He was so angry. He didn't want to go to Spain: he wanted to go to Ireland.

When they got to the hotel they unpacked and then Garry sat down by the window. He sat there for several minutes and then he saw it: it was a leprechaun. He couldn't believe his eyes. He ran outside as fast as his feet would take him.

'Hi! My name's Garry and I'm a huge fan of leprechauns. Could I possibly ask you a question?'

'Hello! My name's Larry, and yes, you can'.

'Why are you in Spain?'

'Almost ever leprechaun came to Spain this year because the weather in Ireland is dreadful.'

After a couple of days Garry and Larry became good friends. On the day Garry had to go back home he asked Larry if he wanted to come back home with him. Larry agreed to come back home with him but he had to travel in Garry's suitcase. When they all got back home Garry ran to his room and let Larry out, but he warned him that he could not come out of his room if his parents were in the house.

After a week Doris went up to Garry's room to get his dirty washing, but instead of dirty washing she found Larry sitting on Garry's bed eating breakfast. 'AHH!!' she screamed.

18 and Under
age category

Journey in the Countryside
By Phoebe Power, aged 16 (Winner)

This bus tastes of cigarette.
Grumbling, dirty-tin monster,
a narrow heap of bitter rust.

I open
one tiny, tight-skinned orange.
The fresh, sparkly smell
is one perfectly round
echo, of the curved citrus
sun outside
in a glazed winter sky that

crumples into wet newspapered
houses dripping petrol;

the bus scratches through the
alleyways. I stare past mud-
spattered windows, as
snow-smooth mountains

swoop, like a young swan's wings
washed in lemon floodlight.

Writer's Block
by Mairi Templeton, aged 17 (Runner-up)

'You have writer's block again?'

Character pulled herself out of the journal, crossed the messy desk, and sat down at the edge.

'Come on.' Character was only big enough to nudge Author's finger, but she tried. 'You know you want to. Be exciting. Blow something up!'

She threw her matchstick arms in the air. Author only stared at the blank paper.

'I can't write,' Author moaned.

Character stood up and paced. For a moment, she looked to be thinking hard. Eventually she collapsed, arms folded, against Author's abandoned pen.

'*Please* try,' she pleaded.

'My characters suck.'

Character sniffed. 'Hardly eloquent for a great writer.'

Author's head dropped to the desk with a thud.

'And I'm a protagonist.'

'Stop it.'

'If anyone should be sulking, it's me. You killed off my friend.'

Author's voice was muffled. 'A necessary plot device.'

'I don't care!'

Character looked up at the roof.

'You could give me a love interest.'

'No!'

'Why not?' Character wheedled. 'You gave my friend one, before you killed her. Why can't I inherit him? *That's* a plot device. '

'This is ridiculous.'

'Why?'

'You shouldn't be talking!'

'Why?' Character laughed at her game.

'You're a character!'

'P-r-o-t-a-g-o-n-i-s-t.'

She stamped her foot, then tried valiantly to lift the pen. Author made no attempt to help.

'You already gave me a voice,' Character panted. She leant her whole weight against the pen. 'And a world. Conflict. Development. Metaphors. Why can't you relax?'

'Because –'

Character slipped. She straightened, brushed herself down, and smiled sweetly.

'Trust me,' she said, drowned by the sound of feet on the stairs. 'Your grammar's awful, but there's nothing wrong with your ideas.'

The study door opened, and Author's mother's head appeared. She looked only mildly confused.

'Who are you talking to?'

All I Need Is Inspiration …
by Louise Hunter, aged 15

I look to the stars for inspiration,
But my stomach rumbles and I put it off,
I look in the fridge for temptation,
A Milky Way bar, all creamy and soft.

I fight with my brain for words on paper,
But find myself daydreaming, miles away,
Now I'm too far gone, I'll do it later,
A pillow, that's enough for one day.

Time stands still as the pen hovers high,
The snow falls and creates a picture outside,
The window turns the promise to a lie,
A blank page, the book shuts and now hides.

I look to the sky for inspiration,
And find the snowflakes release the writer's block,
The fridge is no longer a temptation,
The words flood my brain as I notice the clock ….

Reality
by Louise Hunter, aged 15

Heads rise from the soft comforts of the pillow,
Time to rise and shine,
Legs swing from the bouncy edge of the mattress,
Welcome to the real world.

Feet push down on the pedals of the car,
Time to drive in the sunshine,
Eyes open at the mess of the jam outside,
Welcome to the real world.

Bodies act through the comforts of a character,
Time to show off and shine,
Enemies take the best parts of the play,
Welcome to the real world.

Deliveries
by Amy Pay, aged 17

I may have only been three years old, but I was more than aware that she was coming. Anticipation fuelled the house: Mum's lingered in the deep sighs that followed each gruelling, growl-stricken contraction; Dad's effervesced in the globules of sweat that seeped through his pores as he dithered around gathering tent-like clothes together. Me? I don't remember showing it at all. I wanted a brother.

They said she'd be called Isabella. My pointless moans yearning for an Action Man-loving sibling were abruptly muted when Dad scooped me up and slung me over the garden fence, where I was greeted by our sallow-faced, stooping neighbours. Emergency supplies in the form of a dented tin containing dinner and my playschool flask followed my flailing body over the boundary. As they clambered into our car, bearing smiles that failed to conceal their panic, my parents fled towards Zone B: Maternity. I, Daddy's little 'Ox Girl', was left to fend for myself.

Uncertainty drifted around inside my weary head during that lonesome night. The metallic tang of congealed spaghetti, the sugary scent of blackcurrant squash that diffused through the straw of my flask and the itch of borrowed bed sheets remain a gentle footprint in my memory.

November's six a.m. sting paralysed my toes as Dad lugged me back over the fence towards the car. Our shadow, piggy-back-shaped, stalked us down the hallways of St. Hope's, left, right, left again through the maze. We stopped. I was deposited onto the floor. The towering door opened before me. Warmth smothered my face. I gawped at Mum. She looked drained, pale and clammy yet beatific. Then I noticed her: the bump, the awaited, the other one. I sprinted, like an amphetamine-induced whippet, unleashing a whopping gap-toothed smile and tight embrace onto the newborn.

An Education
by Charles Risius, aged 18

My schooling was grossly conventional. Unfortunately most of the stories that survive from the forties of canes, sherry and buggery are no longer true. I did what was expected of me and found myself at the age of eighteen with a string of letters to put into various forms in the hope of continuing in the same vein for three more years. I pursued various extra-curricular activities and soon discovered that however foully I mutilated the carcass of a Chopin Nocturne on the piano or however many new ways I contrived of losing a football match, I received warm praise. I prided myself on cheating the system, forging a stellar school career without ever genuinely stirring myself. I let certain close friends in on the secret and together we laughed at those who still attempted to 'get an education'.

Blessed with sufficient intelligence to enact this philosophy through school, I found university (not Oxbridge, of course) rather less laughable. At school, when questioned on matters of spirituality I had grandly declared myself a follower of Steiner's anthroposophy, thus ending any further discussion. When I mentioned this to a lecturer in philosophy, I found myself thrown in the deep end and thoroughly drowned. I came out at the end with a third class degree thanks to a prodigious talent for paraphrasing Wikipedia in such a way as to avoid detection.

It seemed natural, therefore, to take a job with an internet essay-writing company where lazy students much like me would pay me, an abject failure at university, to write their dissertations. So far I have earned twenty BAs and eighteen MAs in subjects ranging from theology to engineering. I'm thinking of going back to university.

Regifting
by Mairi Templeton, aged 17

Their favourite song was on the radio.

At the sound of the first chords, she had turned it down so far that the words were barely alive. When her brother had played it, as they had 'jammed' with he on guitar and she on piano, they had played it in F. The piano needed a tune and his solos ground for too long. Each note was still a gift.

She glanced towards the bookshelf. A stack of Christmas presents already lay beside her. She had wrapped them as her mind wandered and there wasn't a crease wrong. The tags were in calligrapher's hand. Even by the tired glow of her lamp, they sparkled.

She had spent hours not thinking of the only gift she was obligated to give.

The bottle of aftershave sat above her, its label faded because he had left it on a windowsill the year before. Since he had won it at the school fair, they had passed it between themselves more times than she could count without laughing. It would appear under alternate trees, wrapped as proudly as any piece of jewellery. Taking it down set her heart throbbing.

The glass was cold. Her fingertips wiped dust from the gold stopper. Over the years, he hadn't had the nerve to use the scent.

She sobbed. He had always faltered on that shift from the B flat. She couldn't sing in any other key.

She cut a square of paper.

There were some things that twenty years of tradition couldn't survive. This wasn't one of them. It was her year to give, so she would wrap the bottle as elegantly as she could. The last thing she did before midnight would be to drive to the cemetery and leave the parcel at her brother's grave.

History, Period Two
by Luke Webber, aged 18

Monday classroom, windows open
    To close-cut grass, shaved mane
    Of a shamed lion; the tribal
    Children crawl its back lice-like,

Red with rushing blood. Throttled tigers,
    History laid out like a rug
    Ready for trampling by the great men
    When they don't take off their shoes.

Armies, invade! Thrust, parry, then retreat
    Into the safe tents of childhood,
    campfires smoking, sleeping bags primed,
    escape from the battles on school fields.

A trophy on the teacher's desk
    For whipping her boys into shape, like
    A vanquished tribesman's hung head
    Mounted on a parlour wall.

For a second the lion roars;
    Foundations tremble as they think
    Of rubble- but a rug won't roar for long.
    Silence at the back of the room.